Kat...

G000144882

POETRY I

The first lick of the lolly

Series Editor
MOIRA ANDREW

M
Macmillan Education

'For David'

Selection © Moira Andrew 1986
Illustrations © Macmillan Education Ltd 1986

All rights reserved. No reproduction, copy or transmission
of this publication may be made without written permission.

No paragraph of this publication may be reproduced, copied
or transmitted save with written permission or in accordance
with the provisions of the Copyright Act 1956 (as amended).

Any person who does any unauthorised act in relation to
this publication may be liable to criminal prosecution and
civil claims for damages.

First published 1986

Published by
MACMILLAN EDUCATION LTD
Houndmills, Basingstoke, Hampshire RG21 2XS
and London
Companies and representatives
throughout the world

Typeset by
Acorn Bookwork, Salisbury, Wilts

Printed in Hong Kong

British Library Cataloguing in Publication Data
Poetry 1: The first lick of the lolly.—(Junior
poetry anthologies; 1)
1. English poetry—20th century
I. Andrew, Moira   II. Series
821'.914'08   PR1174
ISBN 0–333–39201–9

Acknowledgements

The editor and publishers wish to thank the following who have kindly given permission for the use of copyright material:

George Allen & Unwin Ltd for 'Oliphaunt' by J. R. R. Tolkien from **Adventures of Tom Bombadil**. Ian M. Amberson for 'Snowman'. Captain Beaky TM for 'The Bumble Bee' by Jeremy Lloyd from **Captain Beaky Book Volume I** in 1976 by Chappell Music Ltd. Bell & Hyman Ltd for 'Giant' by Ivy O. Eastwick. The Bodley Head for 'Snow-cone' and 'If I Could Only Take Home a Snowflake' by John Agard from **I Din Do Nuttin**. Alan Brownjohn for 'Elephant' from **Brownjohn's Beasts**. Robert Clark for 'Pet Shop' by Leonard Clark. Peter Comaish for 'Looking Up'. Stanley Cook for 'Tadpoles' and 'The Wind' from **Come Along: Poems for Younger Children** published by the author, 600 Barnsley Road, Sheffield, S5 6UA. John Cotton for 'Christmas Eve Night' and 'First Things'. Andre Deutsch Ltd for 'This is the Hand' from **Mind Your Own Business** by Michael Rosen. Faber and Faber Ltd for 'My Aunt' from **Meet My Folks** by Ted Hughes, and 'Monday's Child' from **Clever Polly and the Stupid Wolf** by Catherine Storr. John Fairfax for 'Spacery Rhymes'. Mrs Dorothy Gibson for 'White Cat in Moonlight' by the late Douglas Gibson. Irene Gough for 'Lost – a Lizard'. Joan Gregory for 'White Cat, Black Cat' and 'Tea-time Treat'. David Harmer for 'Alfie'. Harper & Row Publishers Inc. for 'Nora' from **Bronzeville Boys and Girls** by Gwendolyn Brooks. Copyright © 1956 by Gwendolyn Brooks Blakely. John C. Head for 'Monday Morning'. William Heinemann Ltd for 'Blue is the Lake' and 'The Colours Live' from **Hailstones and Halibut Bones** by Mary O'Neill; 'Rabbit and Lark', 'Stones by the Sea', 'Slowly' and 'The Wind' from **The Wandering Moon** by James Reeves, and 'Sunning' from **Crickety Cricket** by James S. Tippett (World's Work Ltd). David Higham Associates Ltd on behalf of Eleanor Farjeon for 'Joseph Fell A-Dreaming' from **Silver Sand and Snow** published by Michael Joseph Ltd, on behalf of Elizabeth Jennings for 'The Radio Men', and on behalf of Russell Hoban for 'Small, Smaller'. Hodder & Stoughton Children's Books for 'Blackberrying', 'The Corn Growing', 'Delicious' from **The Corn Growing** by Leonard Clark, 'Business' from **The Singing Time** by Leonard Clark and 'Johnny's Pockets' from **Helter Skelter** by Alison Winn. Maggie Holmes for 'How Many?' and 'I do love Food'. Libby Houston for 'Ant Town', 'The Key to the Maze' and 'A Black Dot'. Paul Johnson for 'Empty House' and 'Tap Tap Tap Poem'. Jean Kenward for 'Buttons and Beads', 'Gerbil', 'Colours', 'I had a Little Mare', 'Frog', and 'The Visitor'. James Kirkup for 'Thunder and Lightning'. Brian Levison for 'The Magic Snowman'. Gerda Mayer for 'Paper Boat' and 'Swimmer's Song'. Ian McMillan for 'The Sad Bus' and 'This Little Poem'. Spike Milligan for 'Ant and Eleph-Ant' from **A Book of Milliganimals** published by Puffin Books Ltd. Judith Nicholls for 'Plague Frog', 'All Aboard' and 'Breakfast for One'. Leslie Norris for 'Dobbin and Sam' and 'Spell of the Moon'. Oxford University Press for 'Birds in the Forest' from **The Blackbird in the Lilac** by James Reeves (1952). Penguin Books Ltd. for 'Catnap' and 'So Big' by Max Fatchen from **Songs for My Dog and Other People** by Max Fatchen (Kestrel Books, 1980). Copyright © 1980 by Max Fatchen. A. D. Peters & Co. Ltd on behalf of Roger McGough for 'A Cat, a Horse and the Sun' from **After the Merrymaking** published by Jonathan Cape Ltd. Irene Rawnsley for 'Winter Waking'. Michael Rosen for 'Robot', 'Moon', 'Here Comes the Robot', 'Say Please' and 'Digital Watch'. Penelope Rieu for 'The Paint Box' by the late Mrs E. V. Rieu. Howard Sergeant for 'Soft Landings'. Ian Serraillier for 'The Tickle Rhyme' and 'The Kettle Rhyme' from **Puffin Quartet of Poets**. Copyright © 1950 by Ian Serraillier. Sheila Simmons for 'Two Riddles'. Eric Slayter for 'Father Christmas'. The Society of Authors as the Literary Representatives of the Estate of Richard Le Gallienne for 'I Meant to Do My Work Today'. Wes Magee for 'Climb the Mountain', 'Summer Sun' and 'In Bed'. J. Walsh for 'The Spider's Game'.

Every effort has been made to trace all the copyright holders but if any have been inadvertently overlooked the publishers will be pleased to make the necessary arrangements at the first opportunity.

Illustrations by the students of Maidstone College of Art

CONTENTS

First Things

The first lick of the lolly,
The first bite of the cake,
There is something about them
You cannot mistake.

The first day of the holidays,
The first time you wear
Something new, then that feeling
So special is there.

The first time you open
A new comic the smell
Of the ink and the paper
Is exciting as well.

The very first bike ride,
The first dip in the sea,
The first time on a boat
Were all thrilling to me.

The first page of a book,
The first words of a play
And the first thing at morning
When you start a new day.

John Cotton

Snow-cone

Snow-cone nice
Snow-cone sweet
Snow-cone is crush ice
and good for the heat.

When sun really hot
and I thirsty a lot,
Me alone,
Yes me alone,
could eat ten snow-cone.

If you think is lie I tell
wait till you hear the snow-cone bell,
wait till you hear the snow-cone bell.

John Agard

Paper Boat

Make a little paper boat,
Take it to the river,
If it swims and stays afloat,
You will live forever.

Gerda Mayer

Summer Sun

Yes,
the sun shines
    bright
in the summer,
and the breeze
    is soft
        as a sigh.

Yes,
the days are
    long
in the summer,
and the sun
    is king
        of the sky.

Wes Magee

In the Sun

Sit
on your doorstep
or any place.

Sit
in the sun
and lift your face.

Close your eyes and
sun dream.
Soon the warm warm sun
will seem
to fill you up
and
spill over.

Lilian Moore

I meant to do my work today

I meant to do my work today –
But a brown bird sang in the apple tree,
And a butterfly flitted across the field,
And all the leaves were calling me.

And the wind went sighing over the land,
Tossing the grasses to and fro,
And a rainbow held out its shining hand –
So what could I do but laugh and go?

Richard le Gallienne

shower

fierce
  spring
    rain
      full
        gushing
         drain
drab   grey
  steely   puddled
   sky   street
     umbrellas Wellies
       held   for
        high   feet
cars   children
  make   want
   spray   out
     birds   harassed
       huddle   mothers
        away   shout
rain   cats
  becomes lie
    drops   asleep
     slows   plants
      and   drink
       stops   deep
        doors
         open
          wide
           people
           step
            outside

Moira Andrew

The Sad Bus

There's a bus
in the rain
at the end
of the lane.

There are holes
in the side
and the door's
open wide,

and it looks
like a very sad bus.

There's a bus
in the rain
that I won't
catch again.

Left for scrap,
rusting, old,
that wet bus
in the cold,

it looks
like a very sad bus.

Ian McMillan

The Tickle Rhyme

'Who's that tickling my back?' said the wall.
'Me,' said a small
Caterpillar. 'I'm learning
to crawl.'

Ian Serraillier

Rabbit and Lark

'Under the ground
  It's rumbly and dark
And interesting,'
  Said Rabbit to Lark.

Said Lark to Rabbit,
  'Up in the sky
There's plenty of room
  And it's airy and high.'

'Under the ground
  It's warm and dry.
Won't you live with me?'
  Was Rabbit's reply.

'The air's so sunny.
  I wish you'd agree,'
Said the little Lark,
  'To live with me.'

But under the ground
    And up in the sky,
Larks can't burrow
    Nor rabbits fly.

So Skylark over
    And Rabbit under
They had to settle
    To live asunder.

And often these two friends
    Meet with a will
For a chat together
    On top of the hill.

James Reeves

The Spider's Game

The little spider
crawled down the wall
by using its web
so it wouldn't fall.

It crawled to the bottom
and back up again
then thought to himself
what a very fine game.

So he called his friends
to join his game
and they played all day
till night-time came.

And when they had finished
they went off to bed
and left all the wall
covered over in web.

J. Walsh

Blackberrying

'Time to go blackberrying' our mother said
One evening when we were just going off to bed.

We went that Saturday to a place we know
Where year after year the best blackberries grow

At the edge of the common by the steep incline
Up which used to run the old railway line.

They hung in hundreds from the high hedgerows
With tangles of honeysuckle and pink wild rose.

We picked all day, the thorns gave us jags,
But we came home with full baskets and ripe bulging
bags.

There were dark purple stains on our fingers and lips
And our teeth stopped up tight with blackberry pips.

For a week with sharp sweetness our small kitchen
swam
While our mother made sugar and juice into jam.

September is lovely, the real crown of the year
When there for the taking the huge blackberries appear.

Leonard Clark

Buttons and Beads

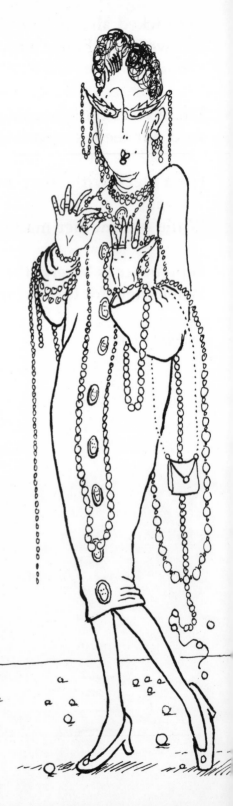

There once was a woman
all buttons and beads
who made a good Seed Cake
without any seeds;

She made a rice pudding
without any rice –
she said 'It's nutritious,
and really quite nice!'

She sewed up a jacket
without any sleeves,
she planted an oak tree
without any leaves;

And, one day, this woman
– why, what do you think? –
she filled up an ink well
without any ink!

She wrote a long letter
without any pen
and when she had finished
she started again.

Each night at her bed time
as likely as not
the hot tap ran cold
and the cold tap ran hot,

So she sewed them both up
without needle or thread,
and slept on the bath mat
without any bed!

Jean Kenward

The Kettle Rhyme

'My kettle's no use any more,' mother said,
  Misery you, misery me,
And she hurled the hole-y thing over the hedge.
  Misery diddle fa-la!

A robin who found it flew down from a tree:
  Merrily you, merrily me,
'This'll do nicely for missus and me.'
  Merrily diddle fa-la!

When father came home he was angry with mother:
  Misery you, misery me,
'I haven't the money to buy us another.'
  Misery diddle fa-la!

Now robin and family, happily settled,
  Merrily you, merrily me,
Peep out – all five – from the hole in the kettle.
  Merrily diddle fa-la!

Ian Serraillier

24

Tap Tap Tap Poem

Steel on floorboards, the
Steel is the song, the
Steel tapping shoes go skipping along.
    Tipety tipety tap tap,
    Tipety tipety hop, the
    Feet go swinging and the poem's hot. The

Body's ticking and the
Knees go swing
Turning in the air in the dancing wind.
    Tipety tipety tap tap,
    Tipety tipety hop, the
    Feet go swinging and the poem's hot. The

Air is laughing, the
Floor is the score, the
Toes are rejoicing and the heels want more.
    Tipety tipety tap tap
    Tipety tipety hop, the
    Feet go a-swinging and the poem's hot.

Dance everybody dance your
Legs away, let your
Knees grow wings and fly away.
    Tipety tipety tap tap
    Tipety tipety hop, the
    Feet go a-swinging and the poem's hot.

Dance   toes
Swing   heels
Dance   toes
Sing   heels
The poem's nearly gone, but the dance goes on.

Paul Johnson

Robot

Humpty Dumpty made a robot.
He made it out of boxes and cans.
He used some buttons for its eyes,
wooden spoons for its two hands.
The robot's mouth was a Macdonald's box
so it could open and shut.
Humpty Dumpty he turned around
and the robot bonked him on the nut.

Michael Rosen

Empty House

In the big black empty
house on the hill
the doors groan . . .
and the windows cry . . .

And from the rooms upstairs
    oh . . .
        ah . . .
and from the cellar
    ah . . .
        mm . . .

And if you listen carefully
you can hear the sound
    of legless feet.

It is never still in
the big black empty
    house on the hill.

Paul Johnson

Pet Shop

At our pet shop you can buy
Things that run and swim and fly,
But never once have I seen them sell
Anything as big as an el-
ephant or albatross,
Crocodile, bear, rhinoceros,
Nor ever a creature as small, alas,
As a kingfisher, or grass-
hopper, earwig, bumble-bee,
Minnow, mole, or common flea.
O, I really think it is absurd
They don't keep a whale or a ladybird.

Leonard Clark

My Friend Luigi

My friend Luigi keeps
   A delicatessen store
And all along the counters are
   Delicious foods galore
Like roll-mops, Russian salad,
   Liver pâté and cole-slaw!

My friend Luigi is
   As fat as a Dutch cheese.
It must be years and years and years
   Since he last saw his knees.
Well, what on earth can you expect
   Among such treats as these?

My friend Luigi likes
   To nibble all day long,
And sometimes when he's feeling gay
   He warbles into song
Although he cannot sing in tune
   And all the notes are wrong.

But my friend Luigi though
   He's short and fat and dressed
In tight green stripey trousers
   And a red and white striped vest
Of all my friends Luigi is
   The one I love the best.

John Smith

Business

Dick Hambone is a grocer,
Who sells tinned fruit and rice,
He weighs the cheese by ounces,
Puts pennies on the price.

Ann Packet has a sweetshop
And lives on chocolate drops,
She'll eat up all the profits
If nibbling never stops.

And Peter Blood the butcher,
He calls my mother, 'Ma'am',
And gives her best New Zealand
When she wants English lamb.

Nell Penn is the postmistress,
Has books and books of stamps,
But sells more bags of firewood,
Saucepans and table lamps.

Tom Salmon, our fishmonger,
Washes his marble slabs
And chops the heads off herrings
And fillets plaice and dabs.

My father's no shopkeeper,
Nor has much work to do,
But though he does no selling,
Minds his own business, too.

Leonard Clark

Hump, the Escalator

Hump, the Escalator, slid
Out of the basement – yes, he did!
Out of the basement unawares,
Flattened a moment, then made a stairs;
Made a stairs that moved and crawled
Up through a runway, narrow-walled.

Here I stood on the floor below,
Then on a stair-step rising slow.
Over the heads of the shoppers then –
Dressed-up ladies and bothered men;

Over the aisles of hats and hose –
Over the shelf-displays I rose!
Suddenly stood on the second floor,
Not on a stairway any more.

Every rider ahead of me
Took it stiffly and solemnly.
Nobody paid a penny's fare –
Or knew they had ridden a Magic Stair!

Anon.

Until I saw the sea

Until I saw the sea
I did not know
that wind
could wrinkle water so.

I never knew
that sun
could splinter a whole sea of blue.

Nor
did I know before,
a sea breathes in and out
upon a shore.

Lilian Moore

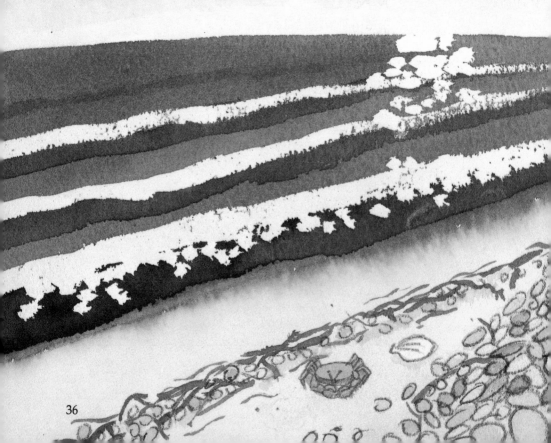

Stones by the Sea

Smooth and flat, grey, brown and white,
Winter and summer, noon and night,
Tumbling together for a thousand ages,
We ought to be wiser than Eastern sages.
But no doubt we stones are foolish as most,
So we don't say much on our stretch of coast.
Quiet and peaceful we mainly sit,
And when storms come up we grumble a bit.

James Reeves

The Song of the Sea Wind

How it sings, sings, sings,
Blowing sharply from the sea-line,
With an edge of salt that stings;
How it laughs aloud and passes
As it cuts the close cliff-grasses;
How it sings again, and whistles
As it shakes the stout sea-thistles –
    How it sings!

How it roars, roars, roars,
In the iron under-caverns,
In the hollows of the shores;
How it roars anew and thunders
As the strong ship splits and sunders,
And sinking, tempest-driven,
On the reef lies rent and riven –
    How it roars!

Austin Dobson

Swimmer's Song

On this grey deserted sea
Every wave has lifted me.
As I love and claim the water,
Surely I am Neptune's daughter.

Gerda Mayer

Sunning

Old dog lay in the summer sun
Much too lazy to rise and run.
He flapped an ear
At a buzzing fly.
He winked a half-opened
Sleepy eye.
He scratched himself
On an itching spot,
As he dozed on the porch
Where the sun was hot.
He whimpered a bit
From force of habit
While he lazily dreamed
Of chasing a rabbit.
But old dog happily lay in the sun
Much too lazy to rise and run.

James S. Tippett

A Cat, a Horse and the Sun

a cat mistrusts the sun
keeps out of its way
only where sun and shadows meet
it moves

a horse loves the sun
it basks all day
snorts
and beats its hooves

the sun likes horses
but hates cats
that is why it makes hay
and heats tin rooves

Roger McGough

41

The Bumble Bee

In his brown and yellow sweater,
Buzzing round the hollyhocks,
Flies a great big bumble bee
Wearing thick black woolly socks.
For bumble bees just live for pleasure
And never work a single day,
Oh what a lovely life of leisure
Just to buzz around and play.
In a big snapdragon snoozing
When the sun is just too hot
Then round the flowerbeds busy cruising
To find another comfy spot.
But there's a problem rather puzzling
And no one's solved the mystery.
Who knits those socks and big striped sweaters?
Can't be lazy bumble bees!

Jeremy Lloyd

Ant Town

Ants live in mazes, not houses.
I lifted the roof of their town:
hundreds of thin black legs
scurrying up and down
black cracks in the brown clay,
some carrying long white eggs.
How can they know their way?
Even the eggs must be black
when I put the stone back.

Libby Houston

The Lizard

If on any warm day when you ramble around
Among moss and dead leaves you should happen to see
A quick trembling thing dart and hide on the ground
And you search in the leaves, you would uncover me.

Thomas Hardy

Lost – a Lizard

Has anybody seen
A lizard in a tin?
A tiny little tin
That you'd keep a lizard in?

Has anybody heard
A lizard in a tin?
A little lizard sounding
As if he's growing thin?

Has *anybody* seen it
Or heard a scratching sound
Of a desperate little lizard
Scrabbling round and round?

Irene Gough

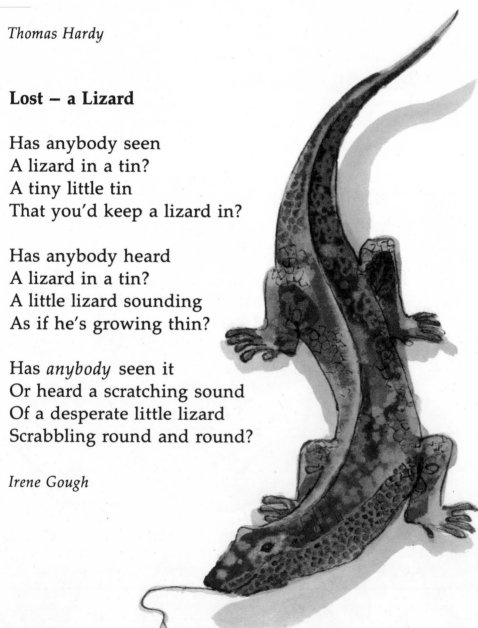

Tadpoles

Tadpoles are fat brown dots
That stand on their tails to nibble weed
Or swish them from side to side
To drive to places to feed:
A head with a tail
Waiting till the body comes,
Waiting for legs
To make it a frog
That climbs from the water on to a stone
And bounces slowly away to a life of its own.

Stanley Cook

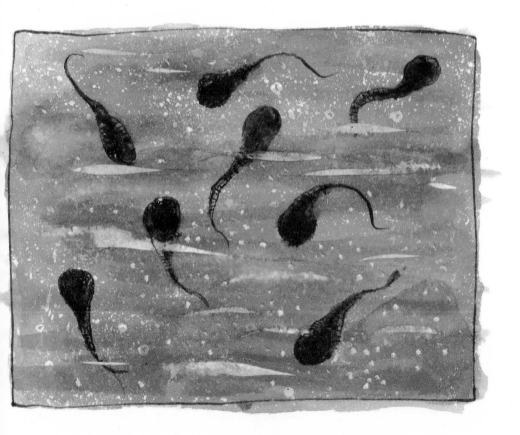

a black dot

a black dot
a jelly tot

a scum-nail
a jiggle-tail

a leg-kicker
a sitting slicker

a panting puffer
a fly-snuffer

a high hopper
a belly-flopper

a catalogue
       to make me

FROG

Libby Houston

Frog

Under the bushes
sleek and slim
there's a middling frog.
I look for him
carefully, turning
stone by stone;
often I find him
quite alone
where the grass is specially
sharp and thin,
and the tangled ivy
closes in,
and the world is shadowed
in green and grey. . . .
He hasn't got anything
much to say,
but his throat moves silently
as though
there were something I certainly
ought to know;
then he flicks his tongue
like a needle, where
the small gnats twirl
in the misty air.
He sometimes jumps.
He sometimes goes
wimbling wambling. . . .
I suppose
a frog is a slithery
thing to be.
I wonder whatever
he thinks of ME?

Jean Kenward

Looking Up

A caterpillar plodded
up a branch mechanically,
munching through fresh leaves
instinctively.

A graceful butterfly came down
to rest upon that bush.
The caterpillar stared in awe
and then it dared to ask:

'Please tell me what you are fine friend,
so beautiful to watch?'
'I'm just your elder brother, Cat,
I used to crawl like you.'

'But you are free to soar up high
and see the splendours of the world.
Please tell me what it's like up there
and how I can be changed to live like you.'

'Oh how can I explain to you
just what it's like from way up here?
You'll have to wait till it's your turn,
preparing while you can for when you fly.'

Peter Comaish

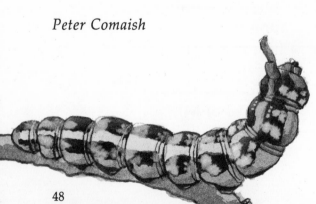

Catnap

My cat sleeps
with her claws
clasped
and her long tail
curled.
My cat twitches
her tabby cheek
for the mice that
squeak
and the milk that
flows
by her pink, pink nose
in the purring warmth
of my cat's world.

Max Fatchen

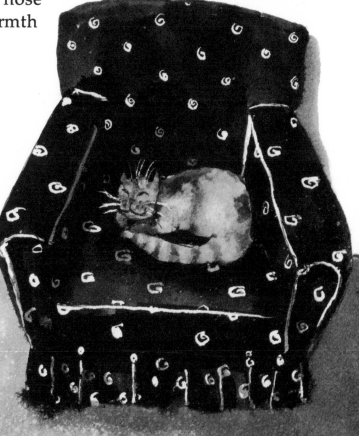

Gerbil

Two brown eyes
peep out of the straw,
a quivering nose
and not much more –
a tail as thick
as a bit of string –
he might be a mouse,
or anything.
Tiny, and most
attentive, he
looks as if
he's measuring me.

'Two blue eyes
look into my straw:
arms and legs
and a good deal more;
clumsy and huge,
I wonder why
it grows so wide
and it grows so high?
What a peculiar
voice it's got –
it is a PERSON
is it not?'

Jean Kenward

Dobbin and Sam

I'm Dobbin
  And I'm Sam
I'm *big* and *strong*
  And I am.
And now
  We'll pull the plough.

The ploughman
  Sets his mark
In the far hedge
  Against the dark,
And straight
  We aim for it.

Down the field
  We plod.
The sharp share
  Turns the sod;
Its shining knife
  Will give the earth new life.

Back we go
  To make another furrow,
A straight one
  And a clean;
So that in Spring
  The brown field will turn green.

Leslie Norris

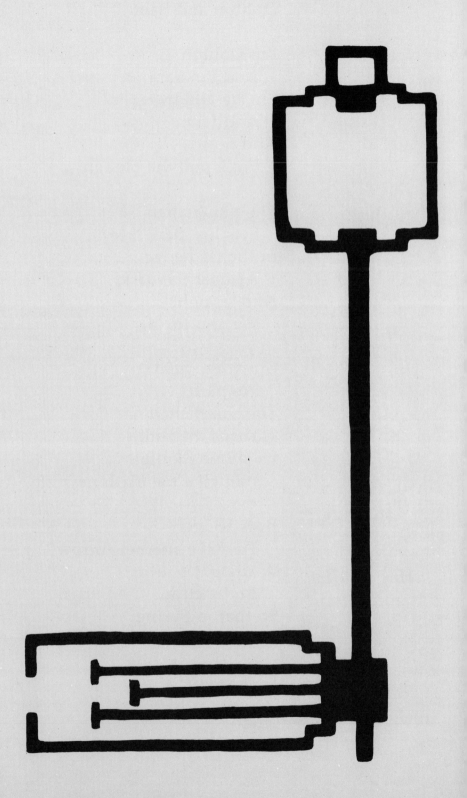

This is the Key

This is the key of the kingdom:
In that kingdom there is a city.
In that city there is a town.
In that town there is a street.
In that street there is a lane.
In that lane there is a yard.
In that yard there is a house.
In that house there is a room.
In that room there is a bed.
On that bed there is a basket.
In that basket there are some flowers.

Flowers in a basket.
Basket in the bed.
Bed in the room.
Room in the house.
House in the yard.
Yard in the lane.
Lane in the street.
Street in the town.
Town in the city.
City in the kingdom.
Of the kingdom this is the key.

Anon.

This is the hand

This is the hand
that touched the frost
that froze my tongue
and made it numb

this is the hand
that cracked the nut
that went in my mouth
and never came out

this is the hand
that slid round the bath
to find the soap
that wouldn't float

this is the hand
on the hot water bottle
meant to warm my bed
that got lost instead

this is the hand
that held the bottle
that let go of the soap
that cracked the nut
that touched the frost
this is the hand
that never gets lost.

Michael Rosen

55

Red

All day
across the way
on someone's sill
a geranium glows
red bright
like a
tiny
faraway
traffic light.

Lilian Moore

Blue is a lake

Blue is a lake,
A sapphire ring,
You can smell blue
In many a thing:
Lupin and larkspur
Forget-me-nots, too.
And if you listen
You can hear blue
In wind over water
And wherever flax blooms
And when evening steps into
Lonely rooms.
Cold is blue:
Flame shot from a welding torch
Is, too:
Hot, wild, screaming, blistering Blue –
And on winter mornings
The dawns are blue. . . .

Part of the poem 'What is blue?' by *Mary O'Neill*.
From *Hailstones and Halibut Bones*
(Worlds Work)

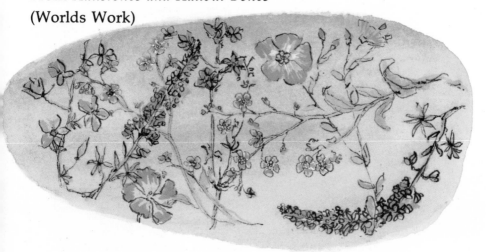

White Cat in Moonlight

Through moonlight's milk
She slowly passes
As soft as silk
Between tall grasses.
I watch her go
So sleek and white,
As white as snow,
The moon so bright
I hardly know –
White moon, white fur –
Which is the light
And which is her.

Douglas Gibbon

The Colours live

The Colours live
Between black and white
In a land that we
Know best by sight.
But knowing best
Isn't everything,
For colours dance
And colours sing,
And colours laugh
And colours cry –
Turn off the light
And colours die,
And they make you feel
Every feeling there is
From the grumpiest grump
To the fizziest fizz.
And you and you and I
Know well
Each has a taste
And each has a smell
And each has a wonderful
Story to tell. . . .

Part of the poem 'Adventures in colour' by *Mary O'Neill.*
From Hailstones and Halibut Bones
(Worlds Work)

Colours

Green days
  blue days
snowy days
  brown days

Sundays
  schooldays
going up to town
  days,

Birthdays
  black days
merry days
  and slow days,

Washing days
  and wishing days
and Well-you-never-know
  days.

Every day's
  a different day,
and every night
  the sun

Goes round behind
  Australia
and brings another
  one!

Jean Kenward

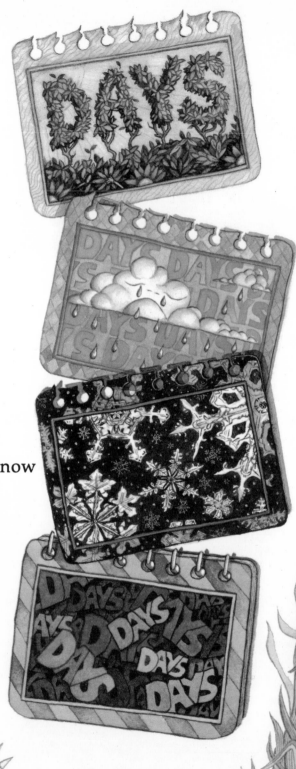

The Paint Box

'Cobalt and umber and ultramarine,
Ivory, black and emerald green –
What shall I paint to give pleasure to you?'
'Paint for me something utterly new.'

'I have painted you tigers in crimson and white.'
'The colours were good and you painted aright.'
'I have painted the cock and a camel in blue.
And a panther in purple.' 'You painted them true.'

Now mix me a colour that nobody knows,
And paint me a country where nobody goes,
And put in it people a little like you,
Watching a unicorn drinking the dew.'

E. V. Rieu

The Key to the Maze

Is it the Maze you're going to?
Here is the key to take you through:
whenever the path divides in two,
keep to the right.

Is that right? Is it true?

I don't know.
But somebody told me so.

Libby Houston

Birds in the Forest

Birds in the forest sing
Of meadows green
They sing of primrose banks
With pools between.

Birds in the forest sing
Of gardens bright
They sing of scented flowers
That haunt the night.

Birds in the forest sing
Of falling water
Falling like the hair
Of a king's daughter.

Birds in the forest sing
Of foreign lands;
They sing of hills beyond
The foamy sands.

They sing of a far mountain
Topped by a town.
Where sits a grey wizard
In a gold crown.

The songs the wild birds sing
In forests tall,
It was the old grey wizard
Taught them all.

James Reeves

The Spell of the Moon

Owl floats through the midnight wood
His terrible voice.
Small creatures alive on the ground
Keep still as ice,
Afraid their bones will be snapped
In his talon's vice.

But the moon hangs in the air,
In the tree's arms,
And she throws on trees and ground
Her silver charms,
Healing the fear of the dark
And night's alarms.

The fox to his lair in the dark
Through shadows will slip,
The shrew and the mole and the vole
To safety creep,
And the moon rides silent and high,
And the wood's asleep.

Leslie Norris

64

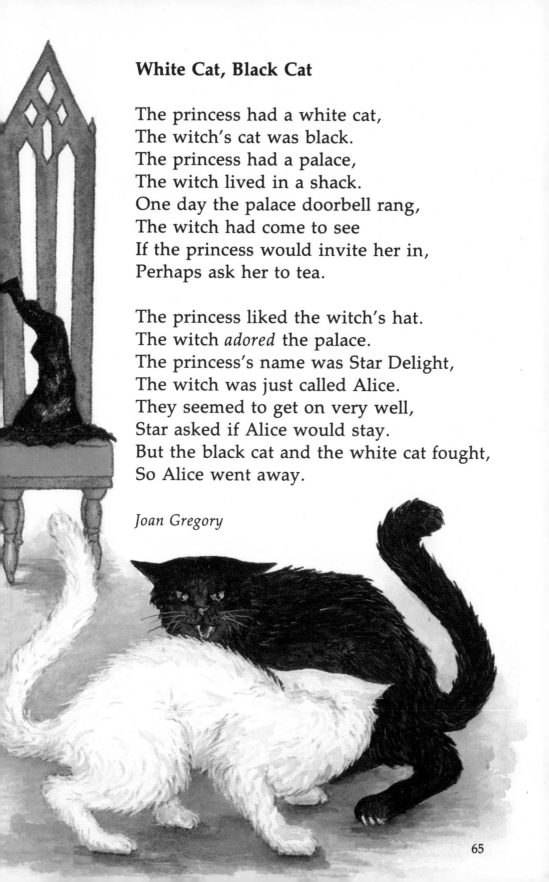

White Cat, Black Cat

The princess had a white cat,
The witch's cat was black.
The princess had a palace,
The witch lived in a shack.
One day the palace doorbell rang,
The witch had come to see
If the princess would invite her in,
Perhaps ask her to tea.

The princess liked the witch's hat.
The witch *adored* the palace.
The princess's name was Star Delight,
The witch was just called Alice.
They seemed to get on very well,
Star asked if Alice would stay.
But the black cat and the white cat fought,
So Alice went away.

Joan Gregory

I had a Little Mare

I had a little mare, sir,
I bought a silver bit,
I sewed a leather bridle
especially to fit;

I fetched a little apple
because she was so shy –
I combed her, and groomed her,
ten hands high.

I tied a knot of ribbon
in her pretty mane,
I rode her, and strode her
up and down the lane:

I rode her and strode her
through the meadow green . . .
down lay the grasses
as if I were a queen;

Up flew the bird folk
clapping on the wing
with Coo, sir, and Caw, sir,
as if I were a king.

Jean Kenward

Slowly

Slowly the tide creeps up the sand,
Slowly the shadows cross the land.
Slowly the cart-horse pulls his mile,
Slowly the old man mounts the stile.

Slowly the hands move round the clock,
Slowly the dew dries on the dock.
Slow is the snail – but slowest of all
The green moss spreads on the old brick wall.

James Reeves

The Corn Growing

Snow no longer snowing,
Wind ends its blowing,
Every stream fresh flowing,
A cockerel loudly crowing,
New grass blades slowly showing,
A bullock deeply lowing,
The chilly evenings going,
And almost without knowing,
The corn growing.

Leonard Clark

Climb the Mountain

Climb
  climb
    the
      mountain
        high,
          touch
            the
              clouds
                and
                  see
                    the
                      sky.
                        Feel
                          the
                            wind
                              against
                                you
                                  blow,
                                    see
                                      the
                                        fields
                                          far
                                            far
                                              below.

Wes Magee

Monday Morning

Moaning, groaning,
mumbling, grumbling,
glowering, showering,
rubbing, scrubbing,
washing, sploshing,
groping, soaping,
howling, towelling,
splashing, dashing,
muttering, buttering,
crunching, munching,
sighing, tying,
brushing, rushing,
cramming, slamming
and off to
school.

John C. Head

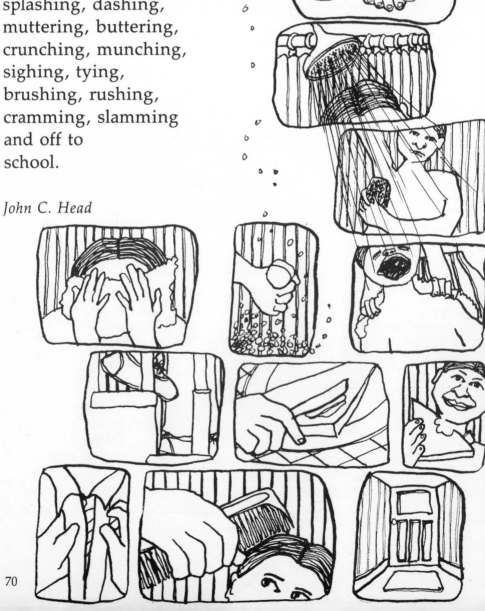

70

Monday's Child

Monday's child is fairly tough,
Tuesday's child is tender enough,
Wednesday's child is good to fry,
Thursday's child is best in pie.
Friday's child makes good meat roll,
Saturday's child is casserole.
But the child that is born on the Sabbath day,
Is delicious when eaten in any way.

Catherine Storr

Johnny's Pockets

Johnny collects
Conkers on strings,
Sycamore seeds
With aeroplane wings,
Green acorn cups,
Seaweed and shells,
Treasures from crackers
Like whistles and bells.

Johnny collects
Buttons and rings,
Bits of a watch,
Cog wheels and springs,
Half-eaten sweets,
Nuts, nails and screws.
That's why his pockets
Bulge out of his trews.

Alison Winn

Alfie

My brother Alfie's had
his hair cut like a hedge,
it sticks up in the middle
and it's spiky round the edge.

He brushes it each morning
and keeps it fairly clean
you'll see him when he's coming,
he's dyed it bottle green.

Now Alfie thinks he's trendy
he thinks he's really cool
looking like a football pitch
as he walks to school.

All the teachers hate him
because he's got green hair,
and other kids they laugh at him
but Alfie doesn't care.

And I think he's fantastic
I think he's really great,
he's my favourite brother
and I'm his little mate.

David Harmer

In Bed

Peter Panda, Little Ted
On the pillow by your head.

Spotty Snake and Farmer Neat
Crowd the blanket at your feet.

Kermit Frog, Old Solly Sand,
Held so tightly in your hand.

Floppy Dog and Soldier Pride
Sound asleep down by your side.

Biscuit crumbs, an apple core,
Comics, books piled on the floor.

Wes Magee

Nora

I was not sleeping when Brother said
'Good-bye!' and laughed and teased my head;
And went, like rockets, out of the door,
As he had done most days before.

But it was fun to curl between
The white warm sheets, and not be seen,

And stay, a minute more, alone,
Keeping myself for my very own.

Gwendolyn Brooks

Winter Waking

Can this be day?
It looks like night
So thin and sulky
Is the light.

A lonely sweeper
In the street
Disturbs the dust
Of last night's feet,

And curtains opened
Splinter wide
Give little sign
Of life inside.

A stubborn car
With cough and wheeze
Resents the turning
Of the keys,

While clockwork birds
Sing 'tin, tin, tin,'
To woo the weary
Morning in,

And singing, singing,
In my head,
How safe it was,
How warm, in bed.

Irene Rawnsley

Grandpa Dropped his Glasses

Grandpa dropped his glasses once
In a pot of dye,
And when he put them on again
He saw a purple sky.
Purple birds were rising up
From a purple hill,
Men were grinding purple cider
At a purple mill.
Purple Adeline was playing
With a purple doll,
Little purple dragon flies
Were crawling up the wall.
And at the supper-table
He got crazy as a loon
From eating purple apple dumplings
With a purple spoon.

Leroy F. Jackson

My Aunt

You've heard how a green thumb
Makes flowers come
Quite without toil
Out of any old soil.

Well, my Aunt's thumbs were green.
At a touch, she had blooms
Of prize Chrysanthemums –
The grandest ever seen.

People from miles around
Came to see those flowers
And were truly astounded
By her unusual powers.

One day a little weed
Pushed up to drink and feed
Among the pampered flowers
At her water-can showers.

Day by day it grew
With ragged leaves and bristles
Till it was tall as me or you –
It was a King of Thistles.

'Prizes for flowers are easy,'
My Aunt said in her pride.
'But was there ever such a weed
The whole world wide?'

She watered it, she tended it,
It grew alarmingly.
As if I had offended it,
It bristled over me.

'Oh Aunt!' I cried. 'Beware of that!
I saw it eat a bird.'
She went on polishing its points
As if she hadn't heard.

'Oh Aunt!' I cried. 'It has a flower
Like a lion's beard –'
Too late! It was devouring her
Just as I had feared!

Her feet were waving in the air –
But I shall not proceed.
Here ends the story of my Aunt
And her ungrateful weed.

Ted Hughes

Moon

Humpty Dumpty went to the moon
on a supersonic spoon.
He took some porridge and a tent
but when he landed
the spoon got bent.
Humpty said he didn't care
and for all I know
he's still up there.

Michael Rosen

Soft Landings

Space-man, space-man,
Blasting off the ground
With a wake of flame behind you
Swifter than passing sound.

Space-man, ace-man,
Shooting through the air,
Twice around the moon and back
Simply because it's there.

Space-man, place-man,
Cruising through the skies
To plant your flags on landscapes
Unknown to human eyes.

Space-man – Race, man,
Scorching back to earth –
To home and friends and everything
That gives your mission worth.

Howard Sergeant

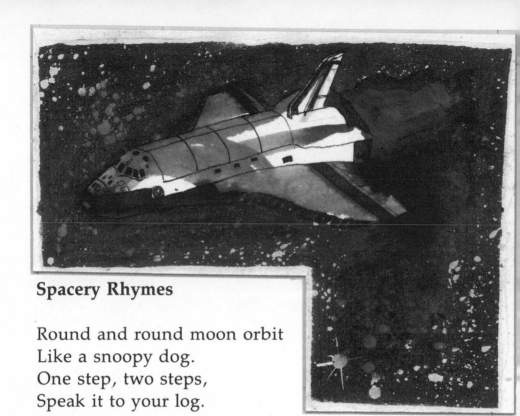

Spacery Rhymes

Round and round moon orbit
Like a snoopy dog.
One step, two steps,
Speak it to your log.

Trickery, trickery dock
Bolts wouldn't lock.

The capsule span
While cameras ran.

Trickery, trickery dock.

Squeeze a tube, squeeze a tube,
Scientist man
Make me a meal
As fast as you can.

Test it and shrink it
And date it with Now

Put it in a shuttle
For me somehow.

Sing a song of spacecraft
Waiting at the Cape.
Four and plenty spacemen
Read computer tape.

When the sums were added
The craft began to move
Now isn't that a lovely sight
For those who live above?

Lunar, lunar module
Where did you wander?
Up a crater down a crater
To take the moon asunder.

There I met a moon-man
Pulling up our flag
So I took him by antenna
And stuffed him in my bag.

John Fairfax

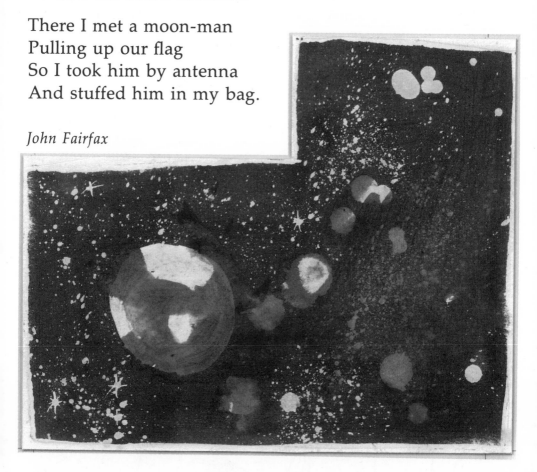

Here comes the robot

Here comes the robot
Bzz Bzz, VROOM!
someone's switched it on
and it's running round the room

Here comes the robot
Bzz Bzz, CRASH!
It's sitting on the table
eating sausages and mash

Here comes the robot
Bzz Bzz, SPLOSH!
It's made the bathroom floor all wet
trying to have a wash

Here comes the robot
Bzz Bzz, BLEEP!
It's sitting in front of the telly
and fallen fast asleep.

Michael Rosen

Plague Frog

I am
  the frog
    that leapt
      from the Nile
        that hopped
          to the palace
            that flipped
              to the bedroom
                that slipped
                  in the sheet
                    that flopped
                      with a smile
                        then nipped
                          at the feet
                            of the king who
                              kept Moses in Egypt.

Judith Nicholls

All Aboard!

Hurry! cried Noah,
and into the ark
rushed

the osprey and the otter
the ostrich and the ox,
the jackal, kangaroo and kite
the scorpion and the fox.
The cacomistle, fresh from sleep
inside his hollow tree,
the cockroach and the cockatoo
the whistling chickadee.
The leopard and the tiger
the squat-nosed liverfluke,
the slow-worm and the glow-worm
and the shy young snake-eyed sheik.
Hinny, hippo, hobby,
hyena, hare and horse,
they all rushed over Noah's plank
before the storm broke loose.

Come in, come in! cried Noah,
Firefly, light these cloudy skies!
In crept grass-snake and glass-snake,
begging birds and mice.

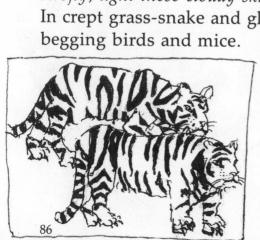

Welcome mealybug and barnacle
and you too, leaf-nosed bat!
Do watch the step – our table's set,
the meal is steaming hot.
I only hope – these skies are black –
our simple ark won't fail!
The swan flew in disdainfully
with Chinese-painted quail.

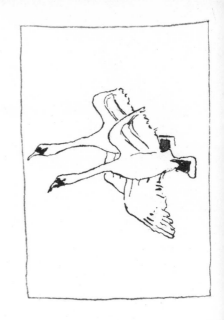

Oh firefly, light our cloudy skies!
Do come in, mole and rat.
If God is willing, here's your home
beside Mount Ararat.

Judith Nicholls

Joseph fell a-dreaming

Joseph fell a-dreaming.
He dreamed of sheaves of grain;
One stood upright like a tree,
The rest bowed down again.

His dreams came with the night
And he told them in the noon.
He dreamed of the eleven stars,
The sun and the moon.

The sun was his father,
The moon was his mother,
Of all the stars, the brightest star
Was Benjamin his brother.

Eleanor Farjeon

Christmas Eve Night

Christmas is when you wake before the light,
Mole up the bed clothes to find what might
Be there in stocking or on bed.
Has Father Christmas been
Or someone in his stead?
Fingers recognize the orange and the nuts,
A book as well is easy to the touch.
But what is this? Its shape will not betray
Its secret, that must wait till day.
So meanwhile, snuggle up,
Pull up the sheets
And wait for the dawn
With its Christmas Day treats.

John Cotton

Father Christmas

He plans to see us once a year
To every child's delight,
And with his presents on his back,
Comes tip-toe in the night.

What was it in the story books
That lent him magic wings
To drive his reindeer through the sky
With bags of gleaming things?

His famous face and bushy beard
And nose of cherry red
Inspired us on the night of nights
Before we went to bed.

What joy was ours on Christmas Day
Those many years ago
When warmly tucked, we listened for
The sleigh bells in the snow.

We left a mince pie near the grate
And sherry in a glass
To greet our aged visitor
And speed him on his task.

Sometimes, of course, he made mistakes
But still, we always thought
That his intentions were the best
With all the gifts he brought.

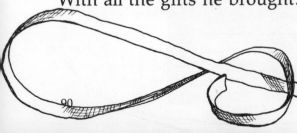

If often puzzled us to find
That he was more than one,
But then, we knew at Christmas time
That magic had begun.

At every time and every place
When I was very young
If I was watching falling snow
Or hearing carols sung,

My mind was busy wondering
How did it come to be
That Santa crossed the whole, wide world
And found his way to – ME.

Eric Slayter

Snowman

When Jason built the snowman
he built him firm and steady,

he christened him Lancelot Fitzjohn
Fitzherbert Sherbet Freddie:

but as he melted he removed
a syllable each day

till only little Lance was left
to sadly fade away.

Ian M. Emberson

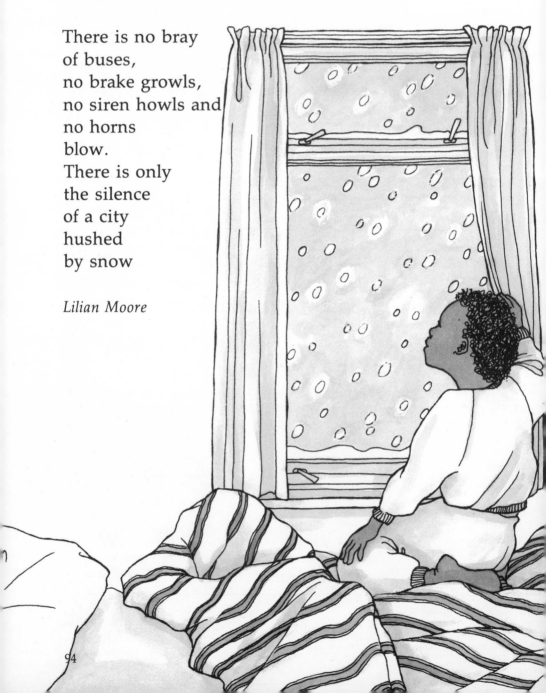

Snowy Morning

Wake
gently this morning
to a different day.
Listen.

There is no bray
of buses,
no brake growls,
no siren howls and
no horns
blow.
There is only
the silence
of a city
hushed
by snow

Lilian Moore

If I Could Only Take Home a Snowflake

Snowflakes
like tiny
insects
drifting
down.

Without a hum
they come,
Without a hum
they go.

Snowflakes
like tiny
insects
drifting
down.

If only
I could take
one
home with me
to show
my friends
in the sun,
just for fun,
just for fun.

John Agard

The Magic Snowman

Christmas comes but once a year –
    You'd think there could be snow!
January or November – yes!
    But Christmas Day – oh no!

So when I woke this morning
    And flung the curtains wide,
Imagine my astonishment –
    A snowman stood outside!

His eyes were two sharp chips of coal,
    About his neck a scarf,
A briar pipe between his lips,
    He gave a jolly laugh.

'My name is Arthur Snowman,
    I'm magic you should know,
I come alive each Christmas Day
    Even without snow!'

I took him in the kitchen
    And made a cup of tea,
And when he'd had a sip or two
    The snowman counselled me:

'Be good as gold, be brave and bold,
    Do as your parents say,
And I will bring you happiness
    Christmas and every day.

'But if you ever tell a fib,
    I'll hear of it for sure
And melt into a puddle
    On your nice clean kitchen floor.'

'I'm always good as gold,' I said,
    'No way could I be better,
And what my parents tell me
    I do to the very letter.'

Now when I get home this morning
    I've got a little chore,
Mopping up the snowman
    From our nice clean kitchen floor.

Brian Levison

The Visitor

There was an old woman
lived all by herself
with a cat and a hen
and a pot on the shelf;
a hen and a cat
and a pot for her tea:
'What more in the world
should I want?' said she.

Well, this old woman
one Christmas night
saw a sledge roll by
so bright, so bright,
heard the sledge bells ring
and a gruff voice sigh,
'It's tired I am
of wind and sky!'

'Then stop you a while,'
the old dame said:
'I've a comfy chair
and a cushion for your head.
I'll boil you an egg
and we'll take a pot of tea.
We'll eat together.
Why not?' said she.

In stepped the traveller
(what was his name?)
with the cat and the hen
and the poor old dame;
he ate and he drank
and he snoozed, and then
with a shuffle of his sack
was gone again.

That wise old woman
she never would tell –
though I guess that she knew
(and she knew quite well)
just WHO came visiting
high and bright
with the moon and the stars
on Christmas night. . . .

Just *who* came visiting,
flecked with snow. . . .
I'm not quite certain,
but I think I know.

Jean Kenward

I can get through a doorway without any key,
And strip the leaves from the great oak tree.

I can drive storm-clouds and shake tall towers,
Or steal through a garden and not wake the flowers.

Seas I can move and ships I can sink;
I can carry a house-top or the scent of a pink.

When I am angry I can rave and riot;
And when I am spent, I lie quiet as quiet.

James Reeves

The Wind

The wind is a wolf
That sniffs at doors
And rattles windows
With his paws.

Hidden in the night,
He rushes round
The locked-up house
Making angry sounds.

He leaps on the roof
And tries to drive
Away the house
And everything inside.

Tired next morning,
The wind's still there
Snatching pieces of paper
And ruffling your hair.

He quietens down and in the end
You hardly notice him go
Whispering down the road
To find another place to blow.

Stanley Cook

Calendar of Cloud

A springtime cloud is
    sudden grief
    a sneak-thief
squeezing the morning dry.

A summer cloud is
    a wishbone
    a fishbone
filleted clean from sky.

An autumn cloud is
    a broomstick
    a doomstock
chasing cobwebs into night.

A winter cloud is
    a bucketful
    a ducking-stool
dowsing every thing in sight.

Moira Andrew

Rain

I opened my eyes
And looked up at the rain
And it dripped in my head
And flowed into my brain
So pardon this wild crazy thing I just said
I'm just not the same since there's rain in my head.
I step very softly
I walk very slow
I can't do a hand-stand
Or I might overflow.
And all I can hear as I lie in my bed
Is the slishity-slosh of the rain in my head.

Shel Silverstein

103

Thunder and Lightning

Blood punches through every vein
As lightning strips the windowpane.

Under its flashing whip, a white
Village leaps to light.

On tubs of thunder, fists of rain
Slog it out of sight again.

Blood punches the heart with fright
As rain belts the village night.

James Kirkup

A Riddle

There was a little green house,
And in the little green house
There was a little brown house,
And in the little brown house
There was a little yellow house,
And in the little yellow house
There was a little white house,
And in the little white house
There was a little heart.

Anon.

Two Riddles

I'm brown
I'm shiny
You long to find me.
In my green shell
I come tumbling down.

You pierce me
And string me,
To school you bring me
To fight your battles
In coat of brown.
                What am I?

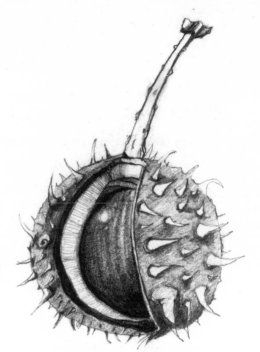

How warmly I cover legs and toes
Snugly knitted
Neatly fitted
One of a pair,
Without me
Your toes are bare!

Guess what I'm doing this special night?
Hanging gently,
Waiting empty.
First, one will fill me –
Then, another will spill me
With shouts of joy!
                What am I?

Sheila Simmons

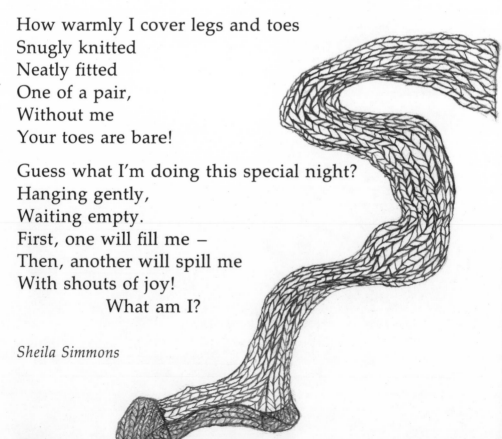

Table Manners

The Goops they lick their fingers,
   And the Goops they lick their knives;
They spill their broth on the table-cloth;
   Oh, they live untidy lives.
The Goops they talk while eating,
   And loud and fast they chew,
So that is why I am glad that I
   Am not a Goop. Are you?

Gelett Burgess

I Do Love Food

I love food piled high on my plate
for dinner, tea I'm never late
yet I am never overweight –
Oh, I do love food

I enjoy fish fingers
and tins of baked beans
I'll even eat cabbage,
sprouts and spring greens.
I eat lots of ice cream,
pink, brown . . . mint's a dream –
Oh, I do love food

I've a passion for pizzas
and beefburgers well filled
I like food that is roasted,
boiled or grilled.
I don't mind it hot, warm
or even well chilled –
Oh, I do love food

You can serve it on plates,
in cups or a dish,
You can offer me beef-steak, chicken or fish,
You can pile on as many chips as you wish –
Oh, I do love food

Potato crisps, pickles, jam tarts, spotted dick,
covered with custard, so yellow and thick.
Oh, dear, I'm beginning to feel a bit sick . . .
But I do love food

Maggie Holmes

Delicious

O, the smell of fish and chips on a winter's night
  with a freezing wind from afar
and then unwrapping the paper and the first wonderful
    bite,
  the tang of salt and vinegar.

And waiting in the steaming shop for them to be fried,
  outside a flurry of snow,
watching the thick creamy batter applied
  to haddock, cod and roe.

A few minutes, chips crispy, and fish cooked golden
    brown,
  wrapped up and taken away,
soon to be eaten dawdling through the white town,
  the end of a lovely day.

And when home and roasting by the fire
give thanks for fisherman, farmer and frier.

Leonard Clark

Pete's Sweets

Pete
will eat
anything
if it's sweet.

Peppermint soup,
or ice cream on toast.

Though what he likes most
is a jelly sandwich
without any bread.

Or instead,
a bubble-gum chop.
Chew your meat thoroughly, Pete.
  'I am. Cancha hear me?' Pop!

Eve Merriam

Say Please

I'll have a please sandwich cheese
No I mean a knees sandwich please
Sorry I mean a fleas sandwich please
No a please sandwich please
no   no –
I'll have a doughnut

Michael Rosen

Tea-time Treat

John likes jam.
His mother said
'Don't put so much
Upon your bread.'
So, instead –
He spread it thickly
On his head.

Joan Gregory

Breakfast for One

Hot thick crusty buttery toast
Buttery toasty thick hot crust
Crusty buttery hot thick toast
Crusty thick hot toasty butter
Thick hot buttery crusty toast
Toasty buttery hot thick crust
Hot buttery thick crusty toast –

with marmalade is how I like it most!

Judith Nicholls

This Little Poem

This little poem has five lines
and five words on every line.
I wrote it out five times
between five o'clock and five past nine
using five different pencils every time
and this little poem tells lies.

Ian McMillan

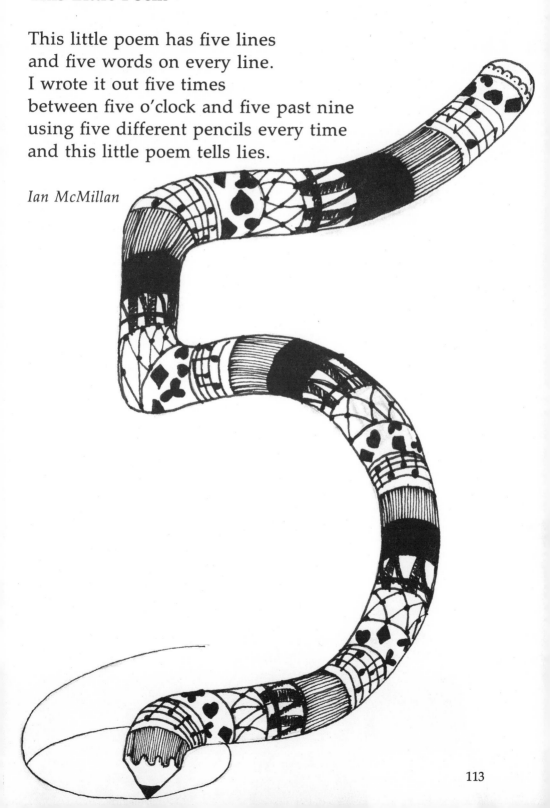

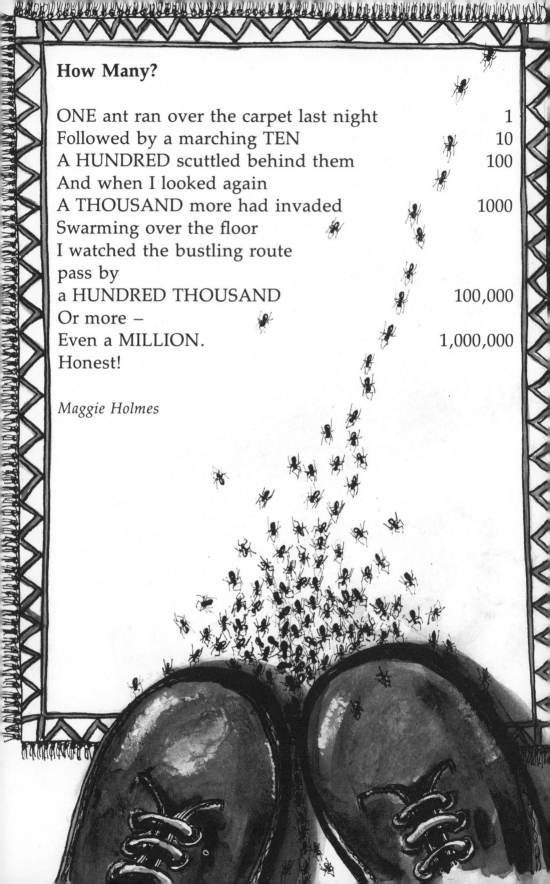

How Many?

ONE ant ran over the carpet last night   1
Followed by a marching TEN   10
A HUNDRED scuttled behind them   100
And when I looked again
A THOUSAND more had invaded   1000
Swarming over the floor
I watched the bustling route
pass by
a HUNDRED THOUSAND   100,000
Or more –
Even a MILLION.   1,000,000
Honest!

Maggie Holmes

SMALL, smaller

I thought I knew all there was to know
Of being small, until I saw once, black against the
 snow,
A shrew, trapped in my footprint, jump and fall
And jump again and fall, the hole too deep, the walls
 too tall.

Russell Hoban

So Big!

The dinosaur, an ancient beast,
I'm told, was very large.
His eyes were big as billiard balls,
His stomach, a garage.
He had a huge and humping back,
A neck as long as Friday.
I'm glad he lived so long ago
And didn't live in my day!

Max Fatchen

Giant

A Giant
  is someone
    ten miles high
      whose feet
        touch the ground
          and whose head
            hits the sky.

And if I
  saw a Giant
    walking down
      our way
        I wouldn't stop
          but I'd run away
            and hide in a doorway
              quiet as a fly . . .

And I wouldn't come out till he'd gone by!

Ivy O. Eastwick

Elephant

It is quite unfair to be
obliged to be so large, so I suppose
you could call me discontented.

Think big, they said, when
I was a little elephant; they
wanted to get me used to it.

It was kind. But it doesn't help if,
inside, you are carefree in small ways,
fond of little amusements.

You are smaller than me, think
how conveniently near the flowers are,
how you can pat the cat by just

halfbending over. You can also
arrange teacups for dolls, play
marbles in the proper season.

I would give anything to be
able to do a tiny, airy, flitting
dance to show how very little a

thing happiness can be really.

Alan Brownjohn

Ant and Eleph-Ant

Said a tiny Ant
To the Elephant,
'Mind how you tread in this clearing!'

But alas! Cruel fate!
She was crushed by the weight
Of an Elephant, hard of hearing.

Spike Milligan

from **Oliphaunt**

Grey as a mouse,
Big as a house,
Nose like a snake,
I make the earth shake,
As I tramp through the grass;
Trees crack as I pass.
With horns in my mouth
I walk in the South,
Flapping big ears.
Beyond count of the years
I stump round and round,
Never lie on the ground,
Not even to die.
Oliphaunt am I,
Biggest of all,
Huge, old and tall.
If ever you'd met me,
You wouldn't forget me.
If ever you do,
You won't think I'm true;
But Old Oliphaunt am I,
And I never lie.

J. R. R. Tolkien

If things grew down

If things grew down
Instead of up,
A dog would grow
Into a pup.
A cat would grow
Into a kitten.
Your sweater would grow
Into a mitten.
A cow would grow
Into a calf
And a whole would grow
Into a half.
Big would grow
Into something small
And small would grow
Into nothing at all.

Robert D. Hoeft

Lisa's Song

Up at the top
Of the tallest tree
I'll build a treehouse
Eventually.

It will ride the breeze
Like the mast of a ship
On the rocking seas,

And I'll look at the world
Below me.

Here I will learn
To talk with birds,
And eagles will come
To know me.

Sam Reavin

The Radio Men

When I was little more than six
I thought that men must be
Alive inside the radio
To act in plays, or simply blow
Trumpets, or sing to me.

I never got a glimpse of them,
They were so very small.
But I imagined them in there,
Their voices bursting on the air
Through that thin, wooden wall.

Elizabeth Jennings

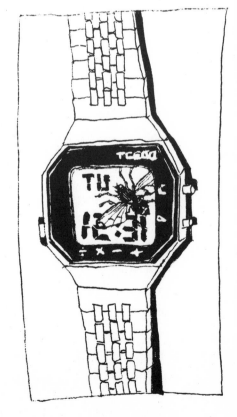

Digital Watch

Digital Fidgetal Botch
a fly got into my watch
the digit digitted
the fly fidgeted
Digital Fidgetal Botch

Michael Rosen

INDEX OF FIRST LINES